NEW FILM THEMES
Playalong *for* Cello

WISE PUBLICATIONS
London/New York/Paris/Sydney/Copenhagen/Berlin/Madrid/Tokyo

Exclusive Distributors:
Music Sales Limited
8/9 Frith Street, London W1D 3JB, England.
Music Sales Pty Limited
120 Rothschild Avenue, Rosebery, NSW 2018, Australia.

Order No. AM975084
ISBN 0-7119-9597-4
This book © Copyright 2002 by Wise Publications.

Music arranged by Simon Lesley.
Music processed by Enigma Music Production Services.
Cover photography by George Taylor.
Printed in Great Britain.

CD produced by Jonas Perrson.
Backing tracks arranged by Danny G, Note-orious & Paul Honey.
Instrumental solos by Justin Pearson.

Your Guarantee of Quality:
As publishers, we strive to produce every book to
the highest commercial standards.
The music has been freshly engraved and the book has been
carefully designed to minimise awkward page turns and
to make playing from it a real pleasure.
Particular care has been given to specifying acid-free, neutral-sized
paper made from pulps which have not been elemental chlorine bleached.
This pulp is from farmed sustainable forests and was
produced with special regard for the environment.
Throughout, the printing and binding have been planned to
ensure a sturdy, attractive publication which should give years of enjoyment.
If your copy fails to meet our high standards,
please inform us and we will gladly replace it.

www.musicsales.com

Amelie

By Yann Tiersen

LA VALSE DE MONSTRES

A Beautiful Mind

By James Horner

ALL LOVE CAN BE

Thoughtfully, cantabile ♩ = 68 **rubato**

Captain Corelli's Mandolin

By Stephen Warbeck

PELAGIA'S SONG

Sadly, tenderly, freely ♩ = 80 **rubato**

Chocolat

By Rachel Portman

PASSAGE OF TIME

Sprightly and balletic ♩ = 90

VIANNE SETS UP SHOP

Folkdance-like ♩ = 106

f *off the string*

Crouching Tiger, Hidden Dragon

By Tan Dun

THE ETERNAL VOW

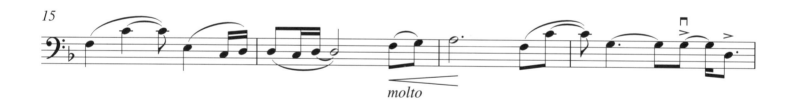

Gosford Park

By Patrick Doyle

PULL YOURSELF TOGETHER

Gladiator

'Honor Him' by Hans Zimmer
'Now We Are Free' by Hans Zimmer, Lisa Gerrard & Klaus Badelt

NOW WE ARE FREE

f more rhythmically

Moulin Rouge!

By David Baerwald

COME WHAT MAY

Steady but appassionato ♩ = 66

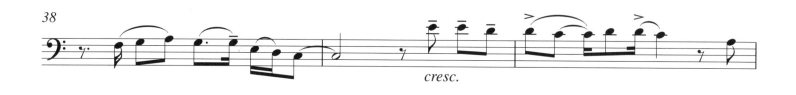

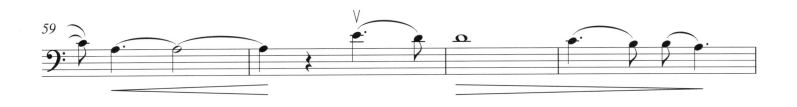

The Royal Tenenbaums

By Mark Mothersbaugh

MOTHERSBAUGH'S CANON

Slowly and thoughtfully ♩ = 63

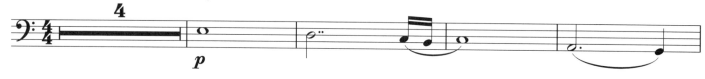

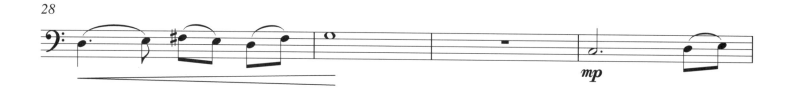

32

cresc.

36

mf

38

40

42

44

dim.

46

49

rit.

p

Ocean's 11

By Claude Debussy

CLAIR DE LUNE

At a slow walking pace ♪. = 50 **rubato**

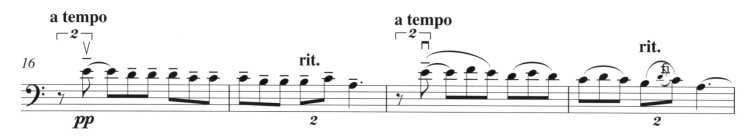

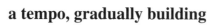

CD Track Listing

Full instrumental performances...

1. Tuning notes

2. Amelie LE BANQUET / LA VALSE DES MONSTRES
(Tiersen) Sony/ATV Music Publishing (UK) Ltd.

3. A Beautiful Mind ALL LOVE CAN BE
(Horner) Cherry Lane Music Ltd. / Universal Music Publishing Ltd.

4. Captain Corelli's Mandolin PELAGIA'S SONG
(Warbeck) Universal Music Publishing Ltd.

5. Chocolat PASSAGE OF TIME / VIANNE SETS UP SHOP
(Portman) Sony/ATV Music Publishing (UK) Ltd.

6. Crouching Tiger, Hidden Dragon THE ETERNAL VOW
(Tan Dun) Sony/ATV Music Publishing (UK) Ltd.

7. Gosford Park PULL YOURSELF TOGETHER
(Doyle) Air-Edel Associates Ltd.

8. Gladiator HONOR HIM / NOW WE ARE FREE
(Zimmer/Gerrard/Badelt) Cherry Lane Music Ltd. / Universal/MCA Music Publishing Ltd.

9. Moulin Rouge! COME WHAT MAY
(Baerwald) Rondor Music (London) Ltd. / EMI Music Publishing Ltd.

10. The Royal Tenenbaums MOTHERSBAUGH'S CANON
(Mothersbaugh) Buena Vista Music Company, USA.

11. Ocean's 11 CLAIR DE LUNE
(Debussy) Dorsey Brothers Music Ltd.

Backing tracks only...

12. Amelie LE BANQUET / LA VALSE DES MONSTRES

13. A Beautiful Mind ALL LOVE CAN BE

14. Captain Corelli's Mandolin PELAGIA'S SONG

15. Chocolat PASSAGE OF TIME / VIANNE SETS UP SHOP

16. Crouching Tiger, Hidden Dragon THE ETERNAL VOW

17. Gosford Park PULL YOURSELF TOGETHER

18. Gladiator HONOR HIM / NOW WE ARE FREE

19. Moulin Rouge! COME WHAT MAY

20. The Royal Tenenbaums MOTHERSBAUGH'S CANON

21. Ocean's 11 CLAIR DE LUNE

To remove your CD from the plastic sleeve, lift the
small lip on the right to break the perforated flap.
Replace the disc after use for convenient storage.